# CONTENTS

I thought it was a friendly ship. But at the last minute they ran up the black flag.

Run up the Jolly Roger, boys!

Aye, aye, Cap'n!

They probably wanted to avoid a fight. Most pirates don't like to risk getting injured or damaging the goods they're after.

But pirates also know that being captured means certain death. So they had good reasons to put up a hard fight.

## THE JOLLY ROGER

Pirate flags were not always black with a white skull and crossbones. The name Jolly Roger comes from the French words *jolie rouge*, which means "pretty red". In the early days of piracy, pirates often flew red flags. Most pirates had their own designs that included symbols of death. The flag designs included skulls, skeletons, swords, bleeding hearts, and more.

These are the crates they stole from our ship.

These are the spare sails. They need to be kept dry. Canvas rots if it becomes too damp.

I can't see my pack anywhere!

Stop right there!

Captain Hyde will be interested in this! It's the lock-up for you two while I tell the Cap'n!

## FOOD AT SEA

Pirates sometimes had fresh food during their voyages. They kept chickens or goats on board when they could, and sometimes caught sea turtles. However, much of their food was salted meat and dry biscuits called hardtack. But after weeks at sea, even these preserved foods went bad. The meat often became rotten, and the biscuits were often filled with bugs called weevils.

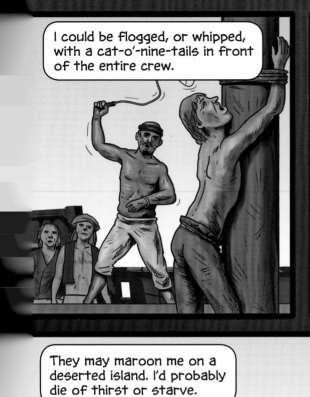

I could be flogged, or whipped, with a cat-o'-nine-tails in front of the entire crew.

They might keelhaul me. They'd bind my hands and feet, and then haul me under the ship. The sharp barnacles would scrape me raw.

They may maroon me on a deserted island. I'd probably die of thirst or starve.

Or maybe they'll just kill me ...

Will they make you walk the plank?

I've never heard of pirates doing that. I reckon they'd just toss me overboard to drown.

13

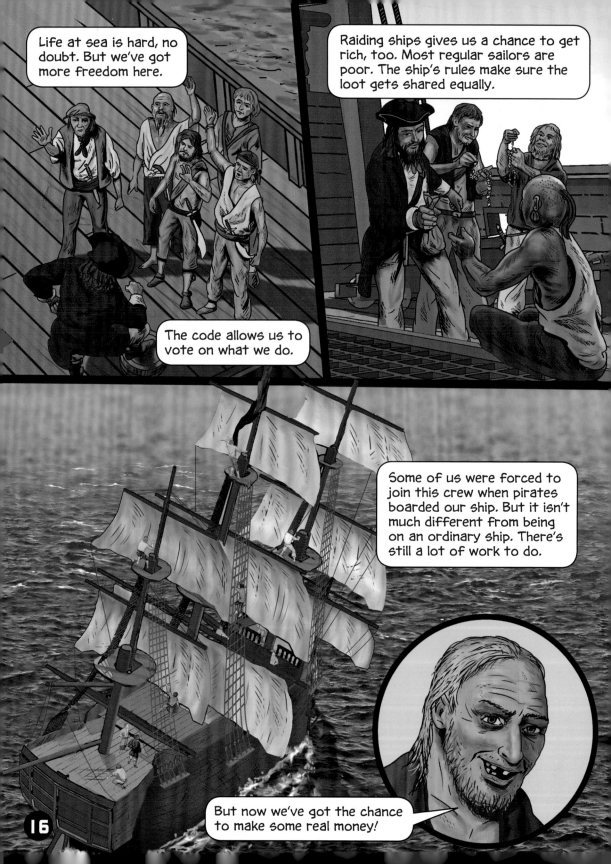

It's not pretty, but it looks like it's healing.

It looks like you'll get paid after all, Bill. According to the code, you'll get 800 pieces of eight.

What will you do?

Maybe I can work in the ship's kitchen. Sometimes men with missing legs become cooks.

Hurry up there! The Cap'n wants you to report on the patient. Let's go.

## TREATING INJURIES

In the 1700s, the only way to treat badly injured arms and legs was to cut them off. A patient was usually held down while the injured limb was sawn off. Brandy or rum was used to control pain, but had little effect. When no doctor was available, the ship's carpenter performed the surgery. Many sailors later died from infections.

Until the 1800s, many governments issued letters of marque to private ships. These licenses allowed them to plunder enemy merchant ships. Such "legal pirates" were known as privateers. Privateers were only allowed to attack enemy vessels during wartime. But when wars ended, some privateers turned to piracy.

Sir Francis Drake was one famous privateer who worked for Queen Elizabeth I. Drake raided Spanish ships for treasure in the late 1500s. The British people considered him a hero. But to Spaniards, he was a cruel pirate.

Pirates voted democratically on all their activities. They even elected their captain and could remove him if they were unhappy with his leadership. To keep order on board ship, pirates made up their own code of laws. The code explained the rules of the ship and how the pirates were to share their loot. It made clear how injured pirates were to be paid. The code also detailed the punishments for breaking any pirate laws.

There weren't many female pirates in history. Anne Bonny and Mary Read are among the few. During battles they wore men's clothing and fought alongside men. Bonny and Read were captured in 1720 with their captain, "Calico Jack" Rackham, and the rest of his crew. Bonny and Read's lives were spared because they were both pregnant. Read died in prison, but Bonny's fate remains unknown.

Pirates sometimes took hostages, as well as cargo. They hoped to get money, or a ransom, for the release of a prisoner. Some captives had to work to pay off their own ransoms.

Pirates still terrorize the seas today, especially near Asia and off the coast of Somalia. Modern pirates don't use swords and sailing ships. Instead, they use modern technology like sonar, machine guns, and speedboats. But just like pirates in the 1700s, they still rob, murder, and kidnap people for ransom.

## MORE ABOUT

**NAME:** Isabel "Izzy" Soto
**INTERESTS:** People and places
**BUILD:** Athletic   **HAIR:** Dark brown
**EYES:** Brown   **HEIGHT:** 1.70 m

**WISP:** The Worldwide Inter-dimensional Space/Time Portal developed by Max Axiom at Axiom Laboratory.

**BACKSTORY:** Isabel "Izzy" Soto caught the humanities bug as a little girl. Every night, her grandfather told her about his adventures exploring ancient ruins in South America. He believed people can learn a lot from other cultures and places.

Izzy's interest in cultures followed her through school and beyond. She studied history and geography. On one research trip, she discovered an ancient stone with mysterious energy. Izzy took the stone to Super Scientist Max Axiom who determined that the stone's energy cuts across space and time. Harnessing the power of the stone, he built a device called the WISP. It opens windows to any place and any time. Although she must not use the WISP to change history, Izzy now explores events wherever and whenever they happen, solving a few mysteries along the way.

#  GLOSSARY

cat-o'-nine-tails  whip with nine knotted cords attached to a handle that was used for punishment

colony  area that has been settled by people from another country and is controlled by that country

hardtack  hard, saltless biscuit once used as food rations for armies and on board ships

infection  illness or disease caused by germs

keelhaul  attach a rope to someone and pull him or her under the bottom of a ship as a punishment

kidnap  capture a person and keep him or her as a prisoner, usually until demands are met

letter of marque  legal document allowing a ship's captain to claim the cargoes of enemy ships

maroon  leave someone alone on a deserted island. Pirates marooned people as a punishment for breaking the rules.

raid  make a sudden, surprise attack

ransom  money that is demanded before a captive person will be set free

sonar  device that uses sound waves to find underwater objects. Sonar stands for sound navigation and ranging.

swab  clean the surface of something, such as the deck of a ship

weevil  type of beetle that is destructive to nuts, fruits, grains, and plants

# FIND OUT MORE

## Books

*Pirate's Handbook* (Usborne Handbooks), Sam Taplin (Usborne Publishing Ltd, 2009)

*Pirate* (Eyewitness Books), Richard Platt (Dorling Kindersley, 2007)

*Pirates* (Horrible Histories Handbooks), Terry Deary (Scholastic, 2006)

*Treasure Island* (Graphic Revolve), Robert Louis Stevenson (Raintree, 2009 – a graphic version of the classic pirate tale)

*William Kidd and the Pirates of the Indian Ocean*, John Malam (QED, 2008)

## Websites

http://www.nationalgeographic.com/pirates/
Find out everything you ever wanted to know about pirates on this National Geographic website.

http://www.dltk-kids.com/articles/famouspirates.htm
Learn more about some of history's most notorious pirates – including two female pirates.

http://www.elizabethan-era.org.uk/pirate-code-conduct.htm
Visit this website to discover more about the pirates' Code of Conduct.

# INDEX